The Girl Who Grew a Sunflower Taller Than Herself (A Sunflower Story)

Written By Dr. Vic

Illustrated by Reagan Baxter

Danni is a girl that likes all the things any kid in the first grade loves…

-she loves her two dogs

-she loves unicorns and rainbows

-she loves to eat pizza and ice cream

-she loves nature

Danni lives in a small house with her mom and she has a neighbor named Shawn.

He is also in the first grade. Shawn is a nice boy and Danni is glad that he lives next door.

Danni and Shawn like to play together after school. They ride their bicycles around the neighborhood. Sometimes they play fetch with Danni's dogs. Sometimes they climb trees.

If it is nice outside, they go to the local park and play on the swings.

Now it is time for summer vacation and school will be done for the year.

Danni finds out that Shawn is going away to camp, for the whole summer. They have about a week to play before Shawn leaves for camp.

Danni says goodbye to Shawn, as he gets on the bus to take him to summer camp.

He tells Danni, "I will be back before we start the second grade." Danni told Shawn, "Have fun at camp."

Danni is bored, without Shawn around to play with.

She just stays in her house on her tablet, looking around, playing games, and watching funny videos on the internet.

One day her mom comes home from work and says to Danni, "You have to play outside, it is not good for you to be inside all the time."

Her mom tells her that she needs to find something to do, because the summer just started.

Her mom asks Danni, "What are some things that you like to do, that you can do outside?"

Danni says that there is not anything to do outside, because she has no one to play with.

Danni's mom remembers that Danni likes nature, so she says, "How about you grow a flower and by the time school starts, it will be fully grown."

Danni has to decide which flower she should grow.

Her mom says, "You can grow roses, and maybe one day when you are older, a boy will bring you a bouquet of roses."

Danni says, "Mom if I want flowers, I will get my own. I do not need a boy to bring flowers to me. I can get anything I want by myself."

Her mom says, "What about tulips?"

Danni thinks they look pretty good, but she wants a flower that will grow really tall."

Danni's mom says, "If you want a tall flower, how about a sunflower?"

Danni really likes the color yellow, so she thinks a sunflower will be perfect.

She gets some sunflower seeds, a watering can, and a flowerpot, to get started.

She plants the seeds two inches deep into the soil. She waters the sunflower seeds every day, but nothing is growing.

She realizes that the sunflower was like her. To be healthy they both need the sun.

Danni puts the sunflower by the kitchen window, so it will be near sunlight.

Soon the seedling starts to grow. During the day it always faces toward the sun, even if Danni moves the flowerpot around.

After a few days, it grows to almost one foot tall.

Danni's mom tells her that the sunflower is too big now for a flowerpot.

They move the sunflower to their backyard and plant it directly into the dirt.

Danni waters the sunflower every day, but if it is a rainy day, it does not need watering.

Too much water will make the sunflower sick.

One day, Danni is outside watering the sunflower and a bee lands on her. Danni is scared and she does not want the bee to sting her. Her mom warned her before, that if a bee ever lands on you to be calm. If you move around too fast, the bee might get nervous and might sting you.

Danni is calm and she blows the bee away. The bee goes over to some other flowers and leaves her alone.

Danni knows that bees need flowers and that flowers need bees. Flowers give bees food, called nectar, and when bees move from flower to flower, they help new plants grow.

She thinks that bees were unfairly feared, because they actually are a flower's helpers.

On a different day, Danni looks outside and sees a squirrel eating part of her sunflower. She does not want the squirrel to eat her flower, but she does not want to hurt the squirrel.

She tries to yell at the squirrel, but it does not care. It knows she cannot catch it. Danni asks her mom what to do and she says, "We can surprise the squirrel and make it never want to eat your sunflower again."

Her mom goes into the kitchen and grabs a jar from inside a cabinet. She sprinkles cayenne pepper on the flower. It does not hurt the sunflower, but when the squirrel takes a bite, it will realize the flower is too spicy. It will run away looking for water.

The squirrel will never try to eat the flower again.

School is about to start in around a month and the sunflower is almost three feet tall. It is almost as tall as Danni now. Danni is so happy. She asks if her mom will take a picture of her with the sunflower. Danni puts on her yellow shirt, so she will be the same color as her sunflower in the picture.

Danni keeps watering the sunflower every day, that it does not rain outside.

It is about a week before school starts and Shawn has come back from camp.

Danni meets Shawn as he gets back and off the bus.

Shawn has grown taller over the Summer.

Danni says, "If you want to see something tall, come see my sunflower in my backyard."

Shawn says, "I didn't know you had any flowers?" Danni says, "I started growing it after you left for camp."

Shawn could not believe how tall the sunflower is. It is much taller than Danni or Shawn.

It is probably 7 feet tall now. It is taller, than most professional basketball players!

Shawn tells Danni, that he will take her picture with the sunflower, because it is so tall now. He cannot get Danni and the sunflower in the same shot because the sunflower is too tall.

Danni goes inside her house and gets a step stool. She has to stand on it, so she can be in the picture with the sunflower. She remembers to put on her yellow shirt for the picture.

It is time for school again. Danni and Shawn are about to start second grade.

Danni is glad she has spent part of the summer outside and she loves growing her sunflower. She hopes that maybe next summer, she can grow more flowers. Not just sunflowers, but lots of different flowers.

After the second week of school Danni comes home and notices that it is getting cold outside. Her sunflower has started to wilt. Soon the sunflower is gone, and Danni is sad.

Her mother tells her that next year she can grow some more flowers. Danni hates to see her sunflower go, but she knows that this is how nature works.

The school year goes by and at the end of second grade, as the summer starts, Danni sees something in her backyard.

She looks at the ground and notices three sprouts.

Danni's sunflower has some seeds that are growing now. Danni is so happy.

She says, "This summer I will get all three flowers to grow 10 feet tall!"

Danni realizes that she has a lot in common with her sunflower. They both need the sun, enough water, and someone who cares for them.

Danni now has a new appreciation for flowers, plants, and nature.

About Dr. Vic

Vitesh "Victor" Enaker is an author and stock options trader currently residing in Lexington, Kentucky. Dr. Enaker is a writer of adult fiction novellas and the first author to write children's books for Seventh Star Press. He has previously lived in the cities of Danville and Mt. Sterling.

A proud member of the Big Blue Nation, Vitesh is a graduate of Transylvania University and he holds a masters and doctoral degree from the University of Kentucky.

He has also been published in the American Journal of Health Studies. He enjoys playing Texas hold'em poker and fishing in various locations around the Bluegrass.

Cover and Illustrations: Reagan Baxter

Editor: Holly Phillippe

Published by Seventh StarChild

ISBN: 978-1-7362781-0-9

Seventh StarChild is an imprint of Seventh Star Press

www.seventhstarpress.com

info@seventhstarpress.com

Publisher's Note:

The Girl who Grew a Sunflower Taller than Herself (A Sunflower Story) is a work of fiction. All names, characters, and places are the product of the author's imagination, used in fictitious manner. Any resemblances to actual persons, places, locales, events, etc. are purely coincidental.

Printed in the United States of America

First Edition

CPSIA information can be obtained
at www.ICGtesting.com
Printed in the USA
BVHW020346121220
595569BV00022B/1312